Court from Peter
with love??
Christmas 1959

NOTHING
BUT
MAX

THE MACMILLAN COMPANY
NEW YORK · CHICAGO
DALLAS · ATLANTA · SAN FRANCISCO
LONDON · MANILA

IN CANADA
BRETT-MACMILLAN LTD.
GALT, ONTARIO

NOTHING BUT MAX

by GIOVANNETTI

THE MACMILLAN COMPANY—NEW YORK—1959

FIRST PRINTING

The sequences on pages 10 through 71 are reproduced by permission of the Proprietors of *Punch*.

The Macmillan Company, New York
Brett-Macmillan Ltd., Galt, Ontario

PRINTED IN THE UNITED STATES OF AMERICA

Library of Congress catalog card number: 59-12839

TO RUSS AND ELAINE

INTRODUCTION

MAX NEEDS NO INTRODUCTION

Jason Robards Jr   Charles M. Schulz

Bill Watterson   C.E. Wilson

Ralph Murphine

Gerry Vanderbilt

Howard Gossage

Moss Hart   Eleanor Roosevelt

Herbert Marshall:

Cyril Ritchard ——   **all say so.**

NOTHING
BUT
MAX

3

2

1

4

5

6

1

2

3

4

5

2

1

3

4

5

6

7

1

2

3

4

5

6

7

8

9

 3

 2

 1

4

5

6

4

5

6

7

6

7

8

2

1

1

2

3

4

5

1

2

3

 5

 6

 7

 8

 9

3

2

1

1

2

3

4

1

2

3

4

5

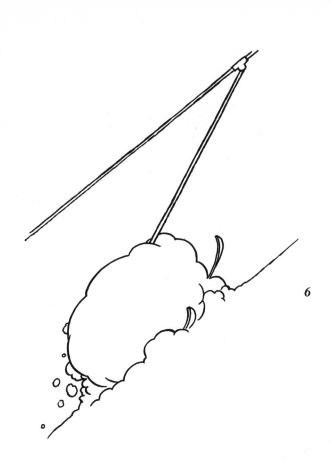

6

7

8

4

5

1

2

3

4

5

6

3

2

1

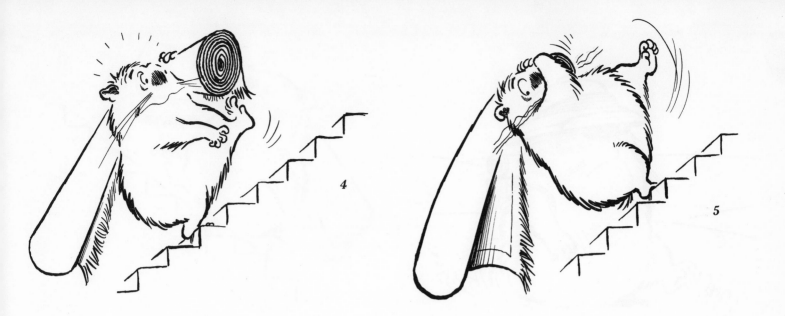

4

5

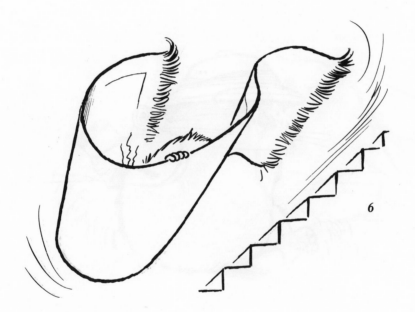

6

7

1

2

3

4

5

3

2

1

4

5

6

1

2

3

4

5

1

2

3

4

5

6

7

8

3

2

1

4

5

6

1

2

3

4

5

6

7

8

1

2

3

4

5

3

2

1

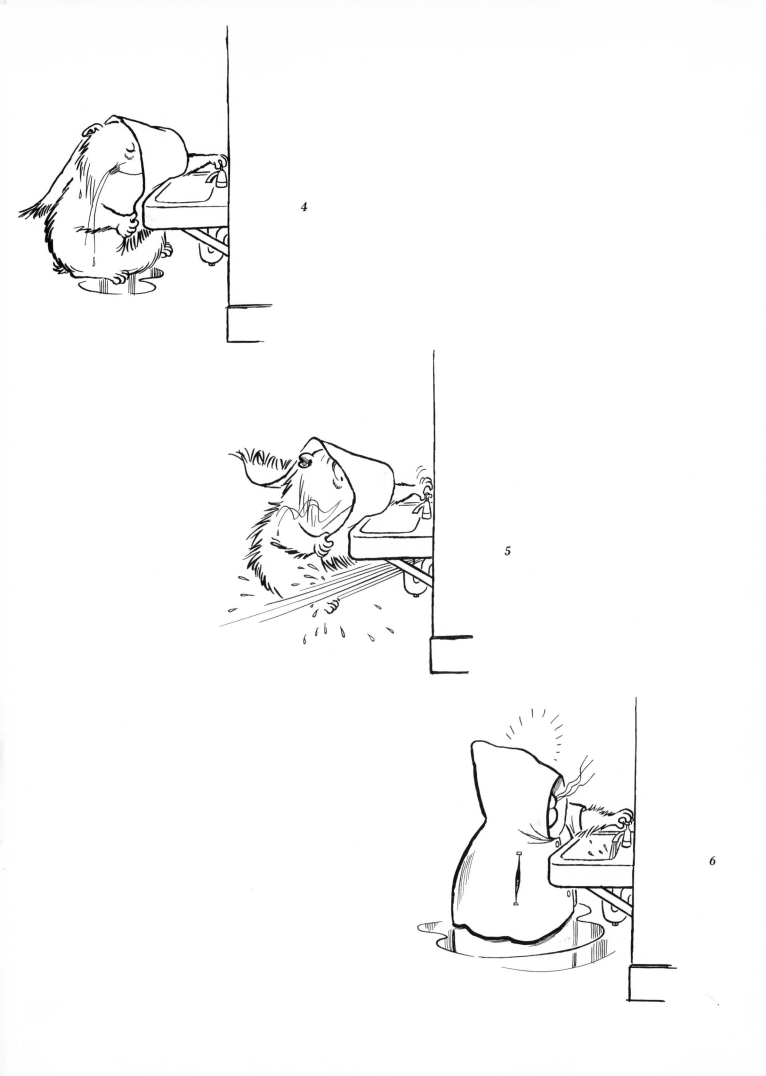

4

5

6

1

2

3

4

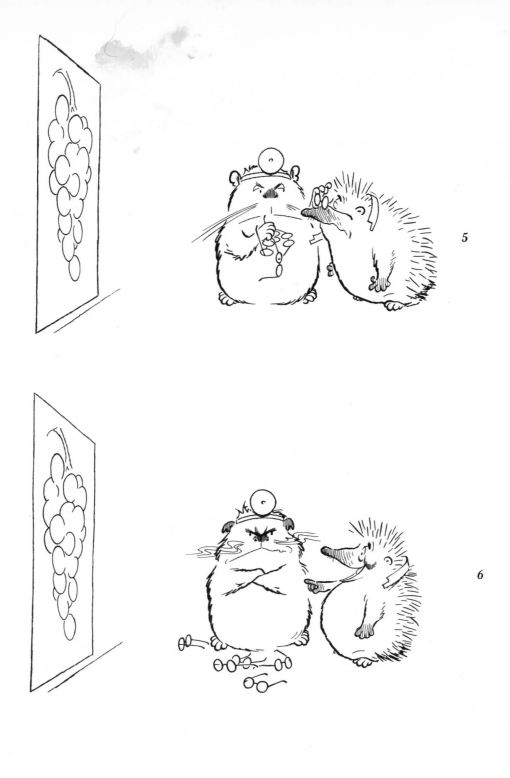

5

6

7

5

6

7

8

1

2

3

4

5

3

2

1

4

5

6

7

1

2

3

4

5

6

7

8

1

4

2

3

5

6

7

8

9

3

2

1

4

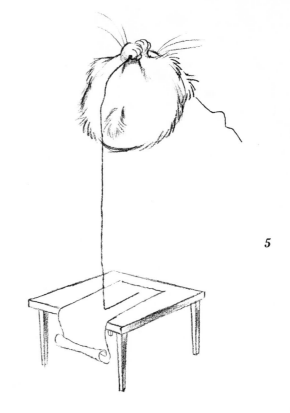

5

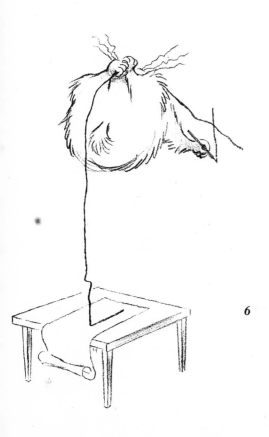

6

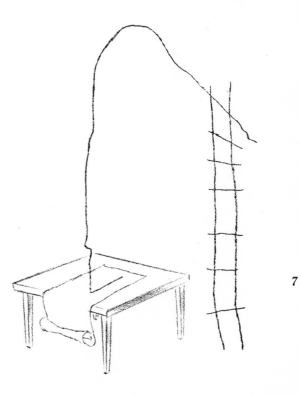

7

4

5

1

2

3

4

 5

 6

 7

1

2

5

4

1

2

3